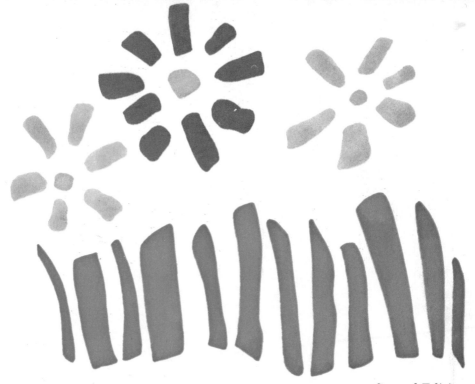

*Second Edition*

# A World of Surprises

Stories and articles by *Elizabeth K. Cooper*

 **Harcourt Brace Jovanovich, Inc.**
*New York   Chicago   San Francisco   Atlanta   Dallas*

 **The Bookmark Reading Program**
EARLY    COOPER    SANTEUSANIO    ADELL

ACKNOWLEDGMENTS: For permission to reprint copyrighted material, grateful acknowledgment is made to the following sources:

THE CURTIS PUBLISHING COMPANY: "Lucy Couldn't Smile" (adapted and retitled: "Linda's Smile") by Margaret Baur from *Jack and Jill* Magazine, May 1965, © 1965 The Curtis Publishing Company. "The Strange Noise" (adapted and retitled: "The Jumping Hat") by Alberta C. Thornton from *Jack and Jill* Magazine, August 1965, © 1965 The Curtis Publishing Company. Adaptation of "Parnell the Pet" by Thomasina Weber from *Jack and Jill* Magazine, February 1967, © 1967 The Curtis Publishing Company.

THE DIAL PRESS, INC.: "Olaf Mails a Letter" adapted from *Olaf Reads* by Joan Lexau, copyright © 1961 by Joan Lexau.

GROSSET & DUNLAP, INC.: "Egbert Learns to Quack" adapted from *The Little Duck Said Quack, Quack, Quack* by Grace and Olive Barnett, copyright © 1955 by Wonder Books, a division of Grosset & Dunlap, Inc.

HARCOURT BRACE JOVANOVICH, INC.: *Two Is a Team* (slightly adapted) by Lorraine and Jerrold Beim, copyright, 1945, by Lorraine and Jerrold Beim. *Timothy Turtle* (abridged and adapted) by Alice Vaught Davis, copyright, 1940, by Harcourt Brace Jovanovich, Inc.; renewed, 1968, by Joseph C. Gill. "At the Zoo" by Myra Cohn Livingston from *Whispers and Other Poems*, © 1958, by Myra Cohn Livingston.

HIGHLIGHTS FOR CHILDREN, INC.: "A New Friend" by Marjorie Allen Anderson from *Children's Activities*, copyright © 1968 Highlights for Children, Inc., Columbus, Ohio. "The Hippopotamus" by Georgia Roberts Durston from *Junior Home*, copyright © 1968 Highlights for Children, Inc., Columbus, Ohio.

PARENTS' MAGAZINE ENTERPRISES, INC.: An adaptation of "The Elephant on the Bus" by Rube Rosen from *Humpty Dumpty's Magazine*, September 1958, copyright © 1958 by Humpty Dumpty, Inc., a division of Parents' Magazine Enterprises, Inc.

CHARLES SCRIBNER'S SONS: "The Handiest Nose" from *Cricket in a Thicket* by Aileen Fisher, copyright © 1963 Aileen Fisher.

WILLIAM JAY SMITH: "Polar Bear" from *Boy Blue's Book of Beasts* by William Jay Smith, copyright © 1956, 1957 by William Jay Smith.

HENRY Z. WALCK, INC.: "Sing a Song of People" from *Songs of the City* by Lois Lenski, © copyright 1956 by Edward B. Marks Music Corp.

The artists in this book and the pages on which their work appears are as follows: Ted Lewin, pp. 7–43; Arnold Genkins, pp. 44–45; Manny Haller, pp. 46, 48, 97, 98, 125–127, 165, 166, 199; Don Almquist, pp. 51–95; Tom Cooke, pp. 101–124; Lynn Sweat, pp. 129–163; Matt Delfino, pp. 169–181, 188–197; Allan Eitzen, pp. 182–186; Kenneth Longtemps, pp. 201–224.

# Contents

## New Friends

## Animals All Around

# Tools

# Animal Talk

## Good Things to Eat

## Two Is a Team

# New Friends

# To the Moon and Back

Dan was looking around the class.
The books were all put away, and the
papers were handed in.

Dan put up his hand. "What do we
do now?" he asked.

"Now we will plan for tomorrow,"
said the teacher. "Tomorrow the
class is going to the moon."

"To the moon!" said the children.

"And back?" asked Dan.

"Yes, to the moon and back, all
in one day," said the teacher.

The next morning the class went off
in the school bus. The bus stopped at
a big building, and the class got off.
A man met the children and took them
into a big room in the building.

The children sat down and were still.
"Now we are going for a long ride," said
the man. "We are going in a rocket."
Dan looked around. He did not see
a rocket. Where was it?

The lights in the room went out, all but the red lights over the doors.

Then a bright flash made the room light up. "Away we go!" said the man.

The children held on to the chairs.

"You must forget that you are sitting still," said the man. "You must think that you are in a rocket. It is moving very fast away from your home planet. You are moving fast, out to the moon."

The children looked up. They saw that
they were moving fast, up into the sky.
The black sky had many bright stars.

Dan looked up and saw the planet they
had come from. It had clouds around it,
and it looked very far away.

Then he saw the moon. It looked big,
big, BIG! It was right before him!

"Get set now for a moon landing,"
said the man, with a smile.

The children held on as they landed
on the moon. Soft lights came on, and
they saw what the moon looked like.

"As you look out at the moon, I will
tell you about it," said the man.

Dan's hand went up.

"What is it?" asked the man.

"I'm going to get out and walk around,"
said Dan, getting up from his chair.
"Then I can see things for myself."

"Dan, sit down," said the teacher.

"But I was just going to look around,"
said Dan. "I won't stay out long."

"I'm glad you like the moon," said
the man, with a smile. "But I don't have
a mask for you. And so you can't
get out of the rocket."

After that, things went all right.
And before long, the room got dark and
the rocket took off for the home planet.
Children began to clap when the rocket
took off from the moon.

Soon the man asked, "Are you all set
to land on the home planet?"

"All set!" cried all but Dan.

He said, "Can't we go to some
other planets?"

Just then the rocket landed and the
lights came on. The children smiled
and clapped. They were glad to be
back on the home planet.

# Linda's Smile

Linda was a happy little girl.
But this morning Linda did not look
happy at all. She did not smile as
she walked up the hill to school.

Before long, Linda met Pam.
Pam was Linda's very best friend.

When Pam saw Linda, she asked,
"Linda, are you mad at me?"

Linda still did not show her smile.
"No, I'm not mad," she said. "I just
can't smile now. I have a surprise
for show-and-tell."

"Oh, good!" cried Pam, who liked
surprises. "I'll tell the others."

Pam ran into the school yard to
the other children. "Linda said she
won't smile," said Pam.

"I can make her smile," said a boy.

"No, you can't," said Linda as she
pulled her lips together.

"Tell me this, Linda," the boy said.
"Why did the bear put on a yellow hat?"

"Why did he?" asked Linda as she opened her lips just a little.

"He had lost all his red hats," said the boy.

"Very funny!" said Linda. But she still hid her smile.

One of the boys began to dance and clap his hands. But Linda still did not smile. She put her hand over her lips and ran into the school room.

Soon all the children were in the
room. The teacher smiled at the class.

The children smiled back at the
teacher, all but Linda. She just sat
and bit her lips.

"First I plan to tell you about
a funny new book," said the teacher.
"Then we will have show-and-tell."

The new book was about a man who
fell into a pond. He hit the water
with a big splash. His friend had to
jump into the water and pull him out.

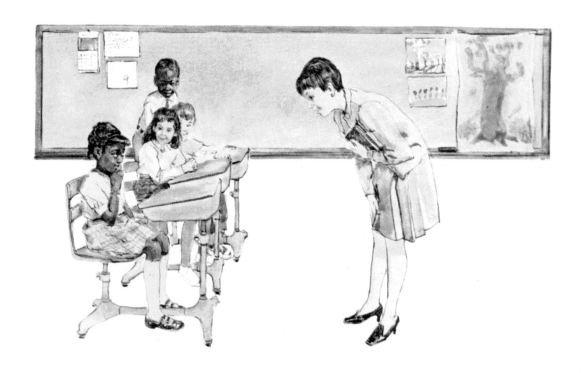

The book was very funny, and the
children liked it. Many of them smiled
and clapped. But Linda just sat with
her sad look.

The teacher looked over at Linda.
"Linda, are you sick?" the teacher asked.
"Where is your happy smile this morning?"

Linda pulled down her top lip and
said, "No, I'm not sick. But I have a
surprise for show-and-tell."

"Then let us have show-and-tell now," said the teacher. "You can be first."

Linda went up for show-and-tell. But she did not tell a thing. All she did was show her happy smile.

That was a big surprise. Linda had lost a tooth!

"Did something hit you?" asked the teacher.

"No," said Linda, "it just came out."

After that, Linda smiled a big smile to show where the tooth had come out.

## Jud Brings Luck

Jud's father was a truck driver.
Jud was going to be a truck driver, too,
as soon as he was as big as his father.
Right now, Jud was just a small boy.
But, as small as he was, the thing he
liked best was his dad's big blue truck.

Day after day Jud asked, "Why can't
I go with you on this trip, Dad?"

And day after day his father said,
"Jud, you are too small to sit all day
in that big truck."

But one day Jud's father planned
to make a trip that was not too long.
He was going in his little red truck,
not his big blue one. And he was going
to let Jud make the trip with him.

"Come on, Jud," he said. "I think
you will bring me luck."

Jud got his cap, and away they went.
First they went on streets in the city.
Then they were out of the city and on
a road where the cars went very fast.

Then, at the top of a very long hill,
luck was not with them. Bump, BUMP!

"Oh, no!" Jud's dad said. "I must
have a bad tire."

The red truck pulled off the road.
"I have to put on a new wheel," said
Jud's dad, getting out of the truck.

Jud's father went to work. He took
off the hub cap. Then he took off the
five lugs and put them into the hub cap.
Next he took off the old wheel and got
a new one from the back of the truck.

Just then Jud opened his door and
jumped down from the truck. He landed
right on the hub cap! Up and over it
went, and all five lugs fell out.

"Get the lugs!" Jud yelled as he
picked up one that had hit a rock.

Jud and his father looked for the other four lugs. But they were lost!

What to do? Jud and his dad sat down to think. Many cars and trucks went buzzing down the road.

"I wish I had stayed home," Jud said. "Now we can't go home until we get the other wheel on."

Jud looked at the wheels on the grass. Then he looked at the three wheels still on the truck. Like a flash, a plan came to him.

"Dad, I can tell you what to do,"
he said. "A wheel with just four lugs
will stay on until we get back home.
Why don't you get a lug from each
of the wheels on the truck?"

Jud was right, and that was what his
father did. He took one lug from each
of the other three wheels. He put the
three lugs on the new wheel. Then he put
on the lug that Jud had picked up, too.

"Now each wheel has four lugs," his
father said. "See, you did bring luck."

"I think it was bad luck, Dad,"
said Jud. "Don't forget, I was the one
who lost the lugs."

The father smiled. "But don't forget,
you did the best thinking," he said.

Then Jud smiled, too.

# Seeing Things?

Donna had played in the lot next to her house all summer. Then one day just before school began, a man came to the lot. He took down the big sign.

"Is someone going to build a house on this lot?" Donna asked the man.

"No," he said. "The people who are moving in don't need to build a house."

"Then, what will they live in?" asked Donna.

"You will see!" the man said.

The next morning Donna ran out
into her yard. To her big surprise,
a bulldozer was in the lot next door.
Donna ran over to look at it.

"What is going on?" Donna asked the
man on the bulldozer. "Are you going
to build a house on this lot?"

"No," the man said with a smile.
"The people who are moving in don't
need to build a house."

"Then, what will they live in?"
asked Donna.

"You will see," said the man. "Now go
away, little girl. I have a job to do."

The next day Donna went out to play
in her yard. Not one car was parked
in her block. Someone had put up
signs that said "No Parking."

Donna was glad to see Policeman Dan.
He was in the street putting up things
to stop the cars and trucks.

"What is going on?" yelled Donna.
"Why are you blocking off the street?"

"Just doing my job," Policeman Dan
said with a smile.

Donna began to think all this was very odd. It was odd that the people who were moving in did not plan to build a house. But why was the street blocked off? And why was the bulldozer on the lot?

Donna went in the house to get her new doll, but she came right back.

"Did I miss something?" she asked Policeman Dan when she came out.

Policeman Dan smiled at Donna, but he said not one thing.

Then Donna looked down the street. "What is that?" she cried.

Donna was so surprised she dropped her doll right in the grass. She raced into the house to get her mother.

"Mom! Mom!" cried Donna. "A house is crawling up the street."

"Yes, yes, Donna," said her mother. "What will it be next? One day you see kings with magic umbrellas. The next day it is a mouse spinning around the moon. You see donkeys in rockets and rabbits in planes and monsters in the yard. Now you see a house crawling up the street!"

"But, Mom, I'm not seeing things,"
Donna said. "Come and see."

She pulled her mother to the yard.

Bump, bump, bump. A house **was**
crawling up the street! A big, big
truck was pulling it.

"You see," said Donna. "I was not
just seeing things."

"They must be moving that house
to the lot next door," Mother said.

"Oh!" said Donna. "So that is it!"

But the best was still to come.
Very soon people came to live in the
house that had crawled up the street.
Donna made friends with the two girls,
and they had a lot of fun together.

# A New Friend

They've taken in the furniture;
I watched carefully.
I wondered, "Will there be a child
Just right to play with me?"

So I peeked through the garden fence
(I couldn't wait to see).
I found the little boy next door
Was peeking back at me.

MARJORIE ALLEN ANDERSON

## Edwin and the Elephants

"Mother, don't let me forget my penny tomorrow," said Edwin. "I'll need a penny a day from now on."

"A penny for what?" asked his mother.

"I can't tell you yet," said Edwin. "I can't tell you until school is out."

"All right," said his mother.

Edwin was in his room in the apartment. His room was filled with elephants!

Edwin had elephant pictures that he had painted. He had clay elephants he had made in school. He had little toy elephants on his bed.

Edwin had many books, too. The ones he liked best were about real elephants. Yet Edwin never saw a real elephant.

"Well, one day I'll see one," said Edwin to himself. "One day I'll have a real elephant."

Many days came and went. Day after day, Edwin painted pictures of elephants. He got new books about real elephants. And he did not forget to bring his penny to school each day.

On the last day of school, Edwin came home with a sheet of paper.

"This is for you, Mother," he said as he handed her the paper. "It tells about the big surprise. All the children in my class are going. You can go, too."

The next morning a bus came to get the children. The teacher and some of the mothers got on the bus with them. The rest of the mothers went in cars.

When the bus got to the park, Edwin was the first to jump out.

"Look, Mother!" he cried. "Now you can see the surprise!"

Edwin's mother saw something moving. It was big and gray.

"Well, Mother," said Edwin. "I have a real elephant at last. What do you think of her?"

"She is a real elephant, all right,"
said Edwin's mother. "But an elephant
like that can't be yours."

"Some of the elephant is Edwin's,"
said the teacher with a big smile.
"He and many other children got it for
a penny a day. Look at the sign."

> **This is Penny. It took a penny
> a day from many children to bring
> her to this city park. A boy who
> likes elephants named her.**

"I'm the boy who named her," said
Edwin with a happy smile.

The children looked at the elephant.
She put her long trunk into some water.
Then, to the children's surprise, Penny
let the water splash over her back.

"I can tell you something else about elephants," said Edwin. "They can pick up things as big as a log. And they can pick up things as small as an ant, too."

As Edwin said this, Penny began moving her trunk around in the grass.

"She must be looking for an ant," said Edwin.

But all the elephant picked up was some grass.

"Look, Penny is eating the grass!" cried Edwin. "She must be hungry."

"Come, Edwin," said the teacher. "We must see the rest of the park now."

"Do I have to?" asked Edwin. "Can't I stay with Penny?"

"We will come back after we ride on the merry-go-round," said the teacher.

Edwin smiled. "I'll never forget this day," he said. "Thank you."

## Olaf Mails a Letter

"Olaf," said his mother, "will you mail a letter for me?"

"What will I get for mailing it?" Olaf asked.

"Not a thing," said his mother. "I am asking you to do it."

"O. K.," said Olaf.

"You can have some cake when you get back," said his mother.

"For mailing a letter?" Olaf said.

"No! Not for mailing a letter. I just happen to have some cake in the kitchen."

"O. K.," said Olaf.

Olaf walked down the block. He did not see a letter box on the street. But he did see a basket that had a sign on it. The sign said

**PUT LITTER IN THIS BASKET**

"I can read," said Olaf. "But they can't spell. They can't spell the word **letter** right."

He dropped the letter in the basket.

Olaf ran home to tell his mother about the basket.

"Oh, no, Olaf!" his mother said. "You put the letter in a litter basket. A litter basket is for old papers and other things that are no good."

"Oh," said Olaf. "Is that what the word on the basket said?"

"Yes, it did," said his mother. "The word was **litter**, not **letter**. Now get the letter and mail it. You can eat this cake as you go."

"O. K.," said Olaf.

A truck was at the basket when Olaf
got to it.  A man was putting the old
papers in the truck.

"Stop!" said Olaf.

Olaf began to tell the man about
the letter and what had happened.

"I'll help you look for it," the
man said.

They looked for the lost letter.
Just then some of the papers fell
from the truck.  Olaf went after them.

"I got it," Olaf cried. "Thank you for helping me."

"Glad to help," said the man.

Olaf put the letter in the letter box. He said, "Why don't they tell us all the words when we first go to school? Then things like this can't happen."

# Sing a Song of People

Sing a song of people
Walking fast or slow;
People in the city,
Up and down they go.

People on the sidewalk,
People on the bus;
People passing, passing.
In back and front of us.
People on the subway
Underneath the ground;
People riding taxis
Round and round and round.

44

People with their hats on,
Going in the doors;
People with umbrellas
When it rains and pours.
People in tall buildings
And in stores below;
Riding elevators
Up and down they go.

People walking singly,
People in a crowd;
People saying nothing,
People talking loud.
People laughing, smiling,
Grumpy people too;
People who just hurry
And never look at you!

Sing a song of people
Who like to come and go;
Sing of city people
You see but never know!

LOIS LENSKI

## Can You Read This?

Wendy came up the walk from school.
At the top of the steps, she opened the
door. Then SLAM! The door went shut.

"Where did you get the new book?"
Wendy's mother asked.

"At school," said Wendy.

"Was it a good day?" asked her mother.

"It was O. K.," said Wendy.

"Then where is your happy smile?"
asked Wendy's mother.

Wendy went to her mother and began to sob. "Pam is mad at me," she said.

"Did Pam get mad at you at school?" asked Wendy's mother.

"Yes," sobbed Wendy. "The teacher got us some new books this afternoon. She let each one of us pick a book to bring home. Pam and I liked a book about pets. Pam put her hand out to get the book, but I grabbed it first. Now Pam is mad at me."

"If you like the book, why don't you sit down and read it?" said Mother.

"But reading is not much fun when your best friend is mad at you," Wendy said.

"I'll tell you what," said Mother. "After you read your book, we can get into the car and go to Pam's house. Then you and she can trade books."

"Oh, Mom!" said Wendy. "Then Pam won't be mad at me. Thanks a lot!"

## Thinking Back

What book do you think Wendy had?

Fun in the City     Dogs and Cats

Happy Days in Summer

What clue in the story helped you
to choose the title of Wendy's book?

## Talking Things Over

1. Tell about a time when your best
   friend was mad at you.
2. What are some of the things friends
   should do for each other?

# New Ways with Words

If you did not know a word in the story, did you try to sound it out?

Did you come to a word you could not sound out? Did the sentences in the story help you?

The words in the box were in the story. Can you read them now?

| | | |
|---|---|---|
| shut | grabbed | steps |
| much | sob | slam |

To read well, you must figure out many words that are new to you.

## Try This

1. Which words in the box have two letters that stand for one sound?
2. Which two words have the same vowel sound as hat?

49

## A Word Pattern

Many words have the same pattern of letters. In the box below, the letter pattern for each word is underlined.

The first letter in each pattern stands for a **vowel** sound. The other letter in each pattern stands for a **consonant** sound. Tell why the patterns are called **vowel-consonant** patterns.

| h<u>ad</u> | th<u>en</u> | s<u>it</u> | sh<u>op</u> | b<u>ug</u> |
|---|---|---|---|---|

A pattern is a clue to the vowel sound a word has. Read the words in the box and listen for the **short** vowel sounds.

Many words with a **vowel-consonant** pattern have a short vowel sound.

## Try This

Read the words in the box again. For each word, think of more words with the same sound and pattern.

# Animals All Around

# The Class Zoo

When Miss Huckleberry was my
teacher, we did things that were fun.
One of the best things we did was to
make a class zoo.

The class zoo began one day when we
were reading about animals in the zoo.
Penny, the girl who sat in back of me, said,
"Why can't we have a zoo in the room?"

Right away Miss Huckleberry said,
"We can." We were all glad she was
going to let us do it.

I put up my hand and said that I had
a big black dog and three cats to bring.
My friend Bill said he had some tadpoles
and a yellow bird.

Then Penny, who likes to talk, said,
"Animals like that don't live in zoos.
They are pets, not zoo animals."

Miss Huckleberry said she was right.
"We will make the zoo animals," she said.

Make zoo animals? Was this one of
Miss Huckleberry's little jokes?

No, it was not a joke. But what were
we going to make the zoo animals from?
It took some thinking!

I was still thinking when Penny
yelled, "Clay!" She yelled it right
in my ear. Boy, she talks a lot.

I had hoped to make the animals
out of wood, but it was just a hope.
The class took a vote and wood lost.
The girls voted for clay, and so did
some of the boys. So it had to be clay.

Miss Huckleberry let me get out the
jar of clay. Other children took around
sheets of paper and dishes of water.

Some people took a little bit of clay
and made small animals. Some people
took a lot of clay and made big animals.

As we were putting the animals away, we just had to smile at some of them. Miss Huckleberry had to smile, too.

The boy who made the hippopotamus did a very good job. So did the boy who made the monkey. But the monkey was as big as the hippopotamus! And so was the spider!

Bill had made the spider with just six legs. Then Penny had to tell him that spiders are not bugs. She then stuck two other legs on the spider.

Bill thanked Penny for helping him. But then Penny had to go and tell him that spiders are not zoo animals.

That was when Miss Huckleberry came to help out. "I think this spider is a zoo animal," she said. "It is as big as a hippopotamus!"

Bill had to smile when the teacher said that.

But Penny is not bad, for a girl.
When the trunk came off my elephant,
she stuck it back on. And when it lost
one of its ears, she made a new one.

Oh, yes, I must not forget to tell
you something else. We voted for the
best animal, and it was my elephant.
It was still a good elephant when one
of its legs dropped off.

For days we worked on clay animals.
Miss Huckleberry helped us a lot, and
we got very good at working with clay.
When we had all the animals we needed,
we made the other things.

I made a lion cage from a hat box.
Other boys made cages, too, but they
were not as big as the one I made.

A girl painted a dish blue to make
a pond for the little hippopotamus.

My friend Bill made a monkey house,
with things for the monkeys to play on.

Penny helped two other girls write signs for the cages. Penny was good at spelling long words like **hippopotamus**.

Then we had to name the zoo, and so we took a vote. After we voted, Penny made a big sign and put it up on the door of the room.

HUCKLEBERRY ZOO

Come one, come all!

COME IN AND SEE THE ANIMALS

Penny let me paint the last word on the sign. I hope I spelled it right.

# Wild Animals in the City

Big wild animals live in the city.
They live in the city zoo, where people
can go to see them.

The zoo animals have come from all
over the world. Some, like the bear
in the picture, are from cold lands.
Some, like the monkey and elephant,
come from hot lands.

Still others, like the red fox, are
from woods not many miles from the city.

In a good zoo, the animals have
a lot of room.  They live as they
did before they came to the zoo.
Many of them live out in the open,
where they can run, hop, and jump.

The zoo animals have things they need
and like.  Monkeys have trees where they
can play and hide.  The hippopotamus has
a pond, where it can splash in the water.
Bears have dark caves to go into on
very hot days.

Other animals have logs to crawl into
and rocks to jump on.  Still others have
grass where they can hide.

Many zoo animals live in the same
building, but not in the same cage.
One building has many cages in it.

The animal cages are like little rooms.
They have back doors so the animals can
go out into a yard. When a door is open,
an animal can go in and out as it wishes.
It can go out in the sun, but it can
come in when it rains and gets cold.

A good zoo is a fine home for many of the animals.

Zoo animals do not have to look for food as all wild animals must do. They get fine food at the zoo, and they never have to go hungry. Some of the food they eat comes from far, far away.

Many animals come back to the cages when it is time to eat. People like to come to the buildings in time to see the hungry animals eating.

It takes a lot of work to run a zoo.
Many people are needed to do the work.

The animals must have food when they
are hungry. They must be looked after
when they are sick. They need ponds,
caves, and other homes to live in.
And the yards and cages must be
in good shape all the time.

A city builds a zoo so that people
from miles around can see wild animals.

Many people never go to the lands
where the wild animals come from.
And so a city brings the wild animals
to the people.

# At the Zoo

I've been to the zoo
    where the thing that you do
    is watching the things
    that the animals do—

and watching
    the animals
    all watching
        you!

MYRA COHN LIVINGSTON

# A Big Baby

The picture shows a mother elephant with her baby. It is a new baby, but it is not very little, is it?

The baby elephant has many things to learn. One of the first things it must learn is how to walk.

The mother elephant helps her baby learn how to walk. She puts her trunk around her baby so it won't fall over.

After the baby elephant learns to
walk, it has other things to learn.
It learns that it must stay with its
mother all the time.

At times, the baby elephant walks too
far away from its mother. The first
time this happens, the mother will go
after her baby and spank it.

The mother elephant spanks her baby
with her trunk. The spanking tells the
baby that it must be good.

When the baby elephant is a little
older, its mother takes it to get water.

When the elephants get to the water,
they walk right into it. The mother
elephant puts her trunk into the water.
She pulls water up in her trunk and
then lets it fall over the baby's back.
What fun this must be for the baby!

In time, the baby elephant will learn
how to take in water with its trunk.
Then it, too, will splash water over
its back.

At first the baby elephant lives on its mother's milk. But when the baby elephant gets bigger, it eats grass.

Elephants walk many miles, eating grass as they go. When they come to a tree, they eat leaves, too.

The best leaves are at the tops of small trees. To get the leaves, the elephant puts its trunk far up into the tree. It pulls down the leaves with its trunk and eats them.

Elephants live in lands where it is hot night and day. But the days are hotter than the nights. That is why elephants walk about in the night. They walk about at night looking for grass and leaves.

When the sun comes up in the morning, the elephants go for water. Then, as the day gets hotter and hotter, it is too hot for the elephants to stay in the sun. And so they go to sleep under the trees.

Day after day, the elephants live like this. They eat, go for water, and sleep. But the big thing is eating.

Elephants are bigger than other land animals, and so they need a lot to eat.

# The Handiest Nose

An elephant's nose
is the handiest nose,
the handiest nose of all—
it curves and sways
in the cleverest ways,
and trumpets a bugle call;
it reaches high
in the leafy sky
for bunches of leaves to eat,
and snuffs around
all over the ground,
and dusts the elephant's feet.

An elephant's nose
is the dandiest nose,
the handiest nose of all
for holding a palm,
when the day is calm,
as an elephant's parasol,
and making a spray
for a sultry day,
and a hose for sprinkling, too,
and a hand to wag
near your peanut bag
when you watch him at the zoo.

Oh, an elephant's nose
is fun to see,
an elephant's nose is fine;
it's clever as ever
a nose can be
but I'm glad it isn't mine.

AILEEN FISHER

## The Hippopotamus

In the squdgy river,
　Down the oozely bank,
Where the ripples shiver,
　And the reeds are rank.

Where the purple Kippo
　Makes an awful fuss,
Lives the hip-hip-hippo
　Hippo-pot-a-mus!

Broad his back and steady;
　　Broad and flat his nose;
Sharp and keen and ready
　　Little eyes are those.

You would think him dreaming
　　Where the mud is deep.
It is only seeming—
　　He is not asleep.

Better not disturb him,
　　There'd be an awful fuss
If you touched the Hippo,
　　Hippo-pot-a-mus.

GEORGIA  ROBERTS  DURSTON

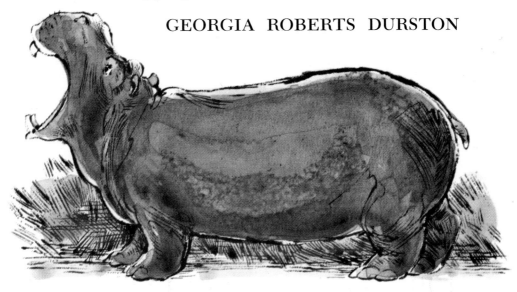

## Polar Bear

The Polar Bear never makes his bed;
He sleeps on a cake of ice instead.
He has no blanket, no quilt, no sheet
Except the rain and snow and sleet.
He drifts about on a white ice floe
While cold winds howl and blizzards blow
And the temperature drops to forty below.
The Polar Bear never makes his bed;
The blanket he pulls up over his head
Is lined with soft and feathery snow.
If ever he rose and turned on the light,
He would find a world of bathtub white,
And icebergs floating through the night.

WILLIAM JAY SMITH

# Wild Animal in the House

"Mother!" called little Wendy Snow
from the bedroom. "What is this under
your bed?"

"Questions! Questions! Questions!"
said Mrs. Snow. "Questions all day long!"

Wendy's mother was in the kitchen.
It was the day of her party, and she
had things to do. This was no time
to have to go running to the bedroom.

"But, Mother," little Wendy called. "Something **is** under your bed!"

"Wendy, why don't you come out in the kitchen and play?" Mrs. Snow called back. "I have work to do, and I can't stop what I'm doing."

"But, Mother," little Wendy answered. "An animal is under your bed!"

At that, Mrs. Snow stopped her work and went fast to the bedroom.

"It may be a kitten," said Wendy, looking under the bed. "But it is dark, and I can't see very well."

"How can it be a kitten? We have never had one," said Wendy's mother. Then she got down to look under the bed.

"My stars!" cried Mrs. Snow when
she saw what it was. "I wonder how
that thing got into the house!"

Like a flash, Mrs. Snow jumped up
and ran, pulling little Wendy with her.
They did not stop running until they
were far out in the yard.

"What happened, Mom?" said Wendy
in surprise. "I was just going to
play with the kitten."

"But that is not a kitten, Wendy,"
said Mrs. Snow. "That is a skunk!"

"But it was just a baby," said Wendy. "Why did we run away?"

"A skunk is a wild animal that lives in the woods," answered her mother. "But the odd thing about a skunk is how it protects itself. When it needs to protect itself, it sprays something that has a very bad smell. The smell is so bad that people can't stay around it."

"Then, how can we have a party with a skunk in the house?" asked Wendy.

"We can't," said Mrs. Snow with a sad look. "I just hope that skunk will leave before my friends come. And I hope it won't think it has to protect itself."

Poor Mrs. Snow! She sat down in the yard, thinking about the skunk. She had to get it out of her house. But how?

# Wendy Had the Answer

Wendy was still in the back yard with her mother. And the skunk was still in the house.

"Did you say a skunk is wild?" asked Wendy.

"Yes, it's wild," said her mother. "But don't ask questions now, Wendy. I have to think."

"But I have an answer this time, not a question," said Wendy. "May I tell you what it is?"

"All right," said Mrs. Snow. "What is your answer?"

"If the skunk is a wild animal, then
the man at the zoo can help," said Wendy.
"Ask him what to do."

"Very good! I'll call the zoo,"
said Mrs. Snow, running to the house.
"You stay in the yard," she called back.

At first the man at the zoo wondered
if Mrs. Snow were playing a funny joke.
But he soon learned that the call was not
a joke at all. Mrs. Snow needed help.

"Do you have some dog food around the house?" asked the man at the zoo.

"Yes," said Mrs. Snow, "but I don't see what that has to do with it. I said I had a skunk in the house, not a dog."

"Right!" said the man from the zoo. "But skunks like dog food, too. So this is what you can do."

When Mrs. Snow came to the door, she did not say a word. But she had a jar of Bozo's dog food in her hand.

"What is that for?" Wendy asked as she walked to the house.

Mrs. Snow smiled, but she still did not say a word. "Sh-sh-sh!" was all she said.

Mrs. Snow went to the bedroom with the can of dog food. She put bits of the food in a path going from the bed, down to the kitchen, and out the door. Then she put bits of dog food in a path from the back door, into the yard, and all the way to the woods.

"Now we will see if that skunk will eat its way out of the house," said Mrs. Snow.

Then she and Wendy went next door and sat very still in the yard.

Before long, the little skunk came out the back door and into the yard. It did not look up. It was happy just to eat and eat and eat. What a fine lunch for that hungry little skunk! It came down the path that went into the woods, eating all the way.

"It worked!" cried Wendy as the skunk
went into the woods. "The man at the zoo
must have had the answer."

"No, Wendy, you were the one who had
the answer this time. It was you who
said to call the zoo. And you can tell
my friends at the party all about it."

"Oh, that will be lots of fun, Mom,"
said Wendy as she danced up and down.
"May I have some cake at the party, too?"

"Questions, questions!" said Mrs. Snow.

# In Time of Danger

Run! Fly! Hide! Fight!
Each of the words tells what some
animals do in time of danger.

The picture shows four wild animals
that are in danger. They are in danger
from the animal that has just come out
of the woods. What will each of the four
animals do if the danger comes its way?

The animals in
this picture can
run fast and far.
In time of danger,
they run.

**KANGAROO**

**ANTELOPE**

**SQUIRREL**

The next two
animals can run
fast, but not far.
In time of danger,
they run and then
hide where they
will be safe.

**PRAIRIE DOG**

This animal
will not need
to run away in
time of danger.
It will stay
and fight.

**WOLF**

Can you read the names of the
animals that run? of the animals
that hide? of the one that fights?

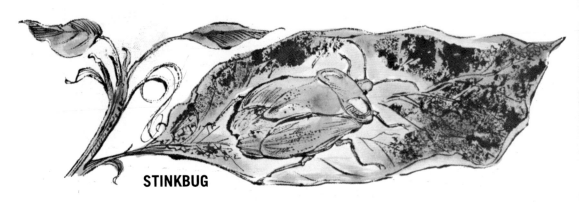

**STINKBUG**

The bug in the picture can't run fast. It is not very good at flying, and it is not an animal that fights. Yet it has a way of protecting itself.

When this little bug is frightened, it sprays something that has a bad smell. Some animals do not like the smell, and so they stay away from the bug.

What other animal protects itself in the same way as this bug?

Some animals have shells to protect them from danger. The land turtle is one animal that will try to protect itself by going under its big shell. Then it will be safe from many dangers.

**TURTLE**

Land turtles hide out in the open,
but not the mud turtles. A frightened
mud turtle sinks down into the mud.
It stays in the mud until it thinks
it is safe to come out.

The picture shows a pond turtle that
is in danger of landing in the boy's net.
If this turtle sees the danger in time,
it will go far down into the water,
where it will be safe.

**TURTLE**

**OPOSSUM**

This animal has a funny way of
protecting itself in time of danger.
It is a wild animal that you may see
in the woods. You may see it in a
zoo, too. Its real name is opossum,
but many people call it 'possum.

The opossum is not an animal to run
away from danger. In time of danger,
it just "plays possum." That is, it
"plays dead." It stays very, very
still as if it were dead.

Do you "play possum" when you try
to make someone think you are sleeping?
Try it sometime — it just may work.

89

# The Cat That Came to School

It was a hot morning, and the door to Room 8 was open. In the room the school children were working. They did not see the big gray and white cat as he walked into the room.

The cat sniffed and looked around. Then, in one jump, he landed on top of the desk by the door. He lay down and went to sleep right on the desk.

At lunch time the cat opened his eyes.
He looked for something to eat.

The children took food from the lunch
boxes and gave it to the hungry cat.
The cat went from desk to desk, eating
what the children gave him.

After lunch, he went out for a walk.
But he was soon back on top of the same
desk where he had sat that morning.

When school was over that afternoon,
the cat went somewhere for the night.
But the next morning when the children
came back to class, so did the cat.
This went on day after day, all year.

Of all the rooms at school, the cat
liked Room 8 the best. When he went
to other rooms, he did not stay long.
He was soon right back in Room 8
on the desk by the door.

In time, the children gave the cat
a name. They named him **Room 8**,
for that was the room he liked best.

The children looked after **Room 8** all
year long. Some days he was wet and cold
when he came to school. Other days he
came in hot and needing a drink of water.
But the children looked after him well.

When summer came and school was over for the year, **Room 8** went away.

He stayed away all summer, but in the fall, **Room 8** came back to school. He went to the same room he had stayed in the year before. He made friends with the new children in Room 8.

This happened, year after year, for 15 years. Many classes moved in and out of the room, but **Room 8** came back to the same room each year.

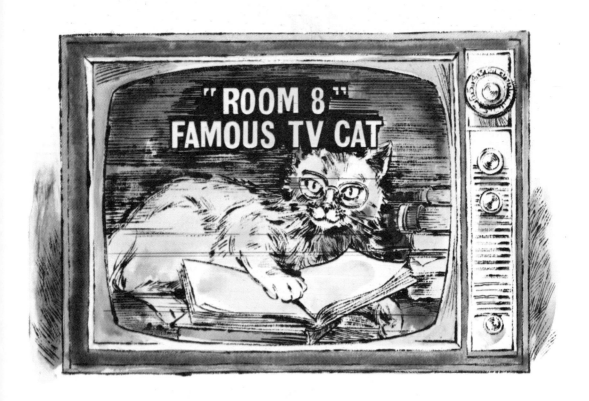

Over the years, **Room 8** came to be
a famous cat. He was on TV many times,
and the shows helped to make him famous.
A book about **Room 8** helped to make him
famous, too. So did his pictures and story
that were in the papers.

For one of the pictures, the children
put eyeglasses on the cat. The picture
showed him with glasses on, looking at
a story the children were reading.

10,000 letters were sent to **Room 8** over the years. Some were from cats. The letters that came from cats were signed with paw prints.

The children helped **Room 8** answer some of his letters. They signed his letters with prints of **Room 8's** paws.

The years went by, and **Room 8** got older and older. At last, when he was 22 years old, he died. This was a very long time for a cat to live.

The day after **Room 8** died, his story was in many papers. One story began, "Room 8, Famous School Cat, Dies at 22."

The famous school cat was missed by many children and teachers.

# Can You Read This?

"Dad," called Pete. "I just made
friends with the boy next door.
When he spoke to me, he asked me to help
him fly his new kite. May I?"

"In a little while," said Pete's father
as he took off his glasses. "It is good
to make friends, but your dog comes first.
Dogs need to run. But look at that big
hole in the gate. Until we do something
about that, your dog has to stay tied to a
post in the yard. So come on now, let us
get to work."

"But we had no gate before we moved,"
answered Pete. "And we never had to
make the dog stay put."

"It is not the same now," said Mr. Clay.
"Now your dog can get in the city street.
He may try to run away, too."

"How come?" asked Pete.

"Well," came the answer. "Some dogs get homesick when they first move to a new home. I have a book about a homesick dog who ran for miles trying to get back to his old home. You can read it after we work on the gate."

"No," said Pete. "I'll save the book until last. I have to run with the dog after I help with the gate. Then before I read the story, I'll help fly the kite."

## Thinking Back

How long had Pete lived in the city?

a long time     not a long time

What were the four things that Pete planned to do? Tell what he planned to do first, next, next, and last.

## Talking Things Over

1. Tell about a time when you and your family moved to a new place.
2. Explain what it means to be homesick.

# New Ways with Words

Sometimes you can't tell what a word means until you read it in a sentence. What does **glasses** mean in this sentence?

**She needs glasses when she reads.**

What words in the sentence gave the clue to the meaning of **glasses**? Is it always that easy to know the meaning of a word? Try it now.

Mother picked up her new glasses. She held them up to the bright light. "Just right," she said. "They will be fine to put milk in."

How far did you have to read to get the meaning of **glasses**? Suppose you were thinking about eyeglasses when you came to the last sentence. What would you have pictured in your mind?

## A Word Pattern

All the words in the box have the same pattern. The pattern is a clue for figuring out the vowel sounds.

Can you read the words now?

| | | |
|---|---|---|
| sa<u>ve</u> | ki<u>te</u> | ho<u>le</u> |
| <u>ga</u>te | whi<u>le</u> | spo<u>ke</u> |

Each pattern that is underlined is a **vowel-consonant-e** pattern. Can you tell why it is called that? Do the words have long or short vowel sounds?

Many words with a **vowel-consonant-e** pattern have a long vowel sound.

## Try This

For each word in the box, think of more words with the same sound and pattern.

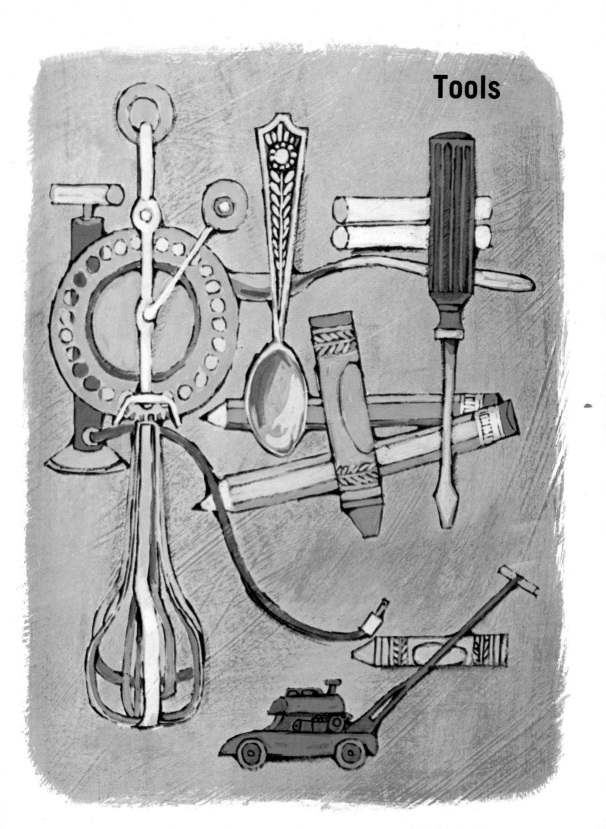

**Tools**

# Tools for Work

For many years people have had work to do. To do work, people use tools.

Tools are held in the hand as people work. The right tools help people do the work they must do.

The picture shows three people who are working in a yard. Each one has a tool to use.

What are the people doing? Can you tell the name of each tool?

Tools are used in the house, too. Mothers use tools when they work in the kitchen. They use them morning, noon, and night.

Some tools, like spoons, are used for many things. A spoon is used to take eggs from hot water. A spoon is used to make a cake. What else are spoons used for?

Name some of the tools your mother uses when she makes your lunch at noon. What tool must she use to open a can? What must she use to cut the food? And then, after she brings the food to you, what tools do you use as you eat?

Many people work away from home.
They go to work in the morning and
work all day long.  As they work, many
of them use tools.

The pictures show people at work.
They work in big buildings and in small
buildings.  They work in shops, in city
parks, and on the streets.

What tools do you see in the pictures?
Tell who uses each tool that you see.

Boys and girls work, too, don't they? They work at home and at school.

The picture shows some of the tools that children use in school. The tools are not new to you because you have used them many times. You use them because they help you do your work.

Name the tool in the picture that you use to cut paper.

What tool do you use when you color?

Tell when you use the other tools.

Are you glad you have good tools to work with? When you have the right tools, some work can be fun.

## Pencils

When you first went to school, you learned how to write. To write, you had to use a tool. What tool do you write with now? Is it a pencil?

Many people call the pencils they write with "lead" pencils. Is that what you call them? If it is, you will think it odd that pencils have no real lead in them.

Real lead is soft and dark gray.
It can be used to make marks on paper.
But the black stuff in pencils is not
real lead at all. It is just called lead
because that is what it looks like, and
because it will make marks on paper.

The lead in pencils is made from a
black stuff that is dug from the land.
Bits of this soft black stuff are mixed
with clay and water to make the lead
for pencils.

Many things are needed to make a pencil. First of all, a slat of wood is needed.

The wood is cut for sticks of lead. How many pencils do you think can be made from this slat of wood?

A stick of lead is then put into each of the cuts. Each stick of lead is as long as a new pencil.

Now a slat of wood is put on top of the first slat. The two slats of wood are stuck together.

At last the wood is cut into three parts. Each of the three parts is then cut into the shape of a pencil.

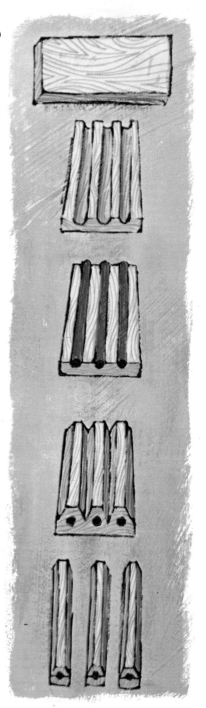

After the wood is shaped
to make a pencil, it is
painted a bright color.
Then the eraser is put on.
A band is put around the
eraser to make it stay
on the pencil.

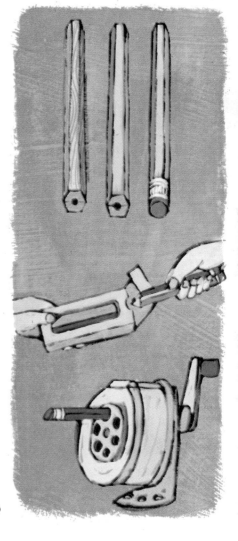

After that, the pencils
are put into boxes. They
are sent to people in many
parts of the world.

As you write with a
pencil, what happens to
the lead? What tool is
used to cut away the wood?

A pencil gets smaller and smaller as
it is used. It is hard to write with a
pencil after it gets very small.
Then it is time to get a new one.

A STICK OF CHALK

## A Stick of Chalk

When people write, they do not
use a pencil all the time, do they?
At times they use chalk.

A stick of chalk is not a good tool
for writing on paper. What do people
write on when they write with chalk?

Real chalk is a soft, white rock. The first chalk used for writing was a bit of this rock. But real chalk was not very good for writing.

After many years, a man learned how to make chalk that was good for writing. He made the chalk right in his kitchen.

This man took bits of the rock and made a fine, white powder from them. Then he put the fine, white powder into a set of molds. Each mold was shaped like a stick of chalk.

After the molds were all filled with
white powder, they were put into a very
hot oven. They were put into the oven
to bake the powder. The powder was
baked to make it hard.

The picture shows the man taking
the molds from the oven. Can you see
the hard stick of chalk in each mold?

Now all chalk for school is made from
white powder. But chalk is no longer
made in a man's kitchen. Now it is made
in big plants where many sticks of chalk
can be made at the same time.

Sticks of chalk can be made in many
colors. To make yellow chalk, yellow
powder is mixed with the white powder.
Red, green, and blue powder is used
to make chalk of other colors.

# How to Make a Chalk Picture

Chalk pictures are bright, and they are fun to make. For a good picture, use a big sheet of paper. Use colors that are right for the things that will be in your picture.

When the picture is made, shake it. Some of the powder will fall from the sheet of paper.

To make the chalk stick to your paper, you may wet the chalk before you use it. Working with wet sticks of chalk makes the colors look brighter.

You can mix chalk colors right on your paper. Just rub your hands over the paper after you put the colors on.

Sticks of chalk are good tools to use when children work together on one big picture. Chalk pictures are good ones to put up around the room.

# Crayons

When you are in school, you work hard each day. You read, write, spell, and do other things. Of all the things you do in school, what do you like best?

Many children your age like to color. What tool do you think they use when they color?

Some little children use crayons before they learn to use pencils. But crayons are used by people of all ages, not just by little children.

116

Working with a crayon is not the same
as working with pencils or with chalk.
Marks made with pencils may be erased,
and chalk marks may be rubbed together.

But crayon marks cannot be erased or
rubbed together. This is because crayons
are made of wax.

To make crayons, the first job is to
get the wax and melt it. Wax melts when
it gets very hot. As it gets hot, it gets
softer and softer. Then it melts.

Colors are mixed with the melted wax.
Blue coloring is used for blue crayons,
red coloring for red crayons, and so on.

The melted wax is put into molds
that have the same shapes as crayons.
After each mold is filled, the wax has
to cool. As it cools, the wax gets hard.
The hard sticks of wax are crayons.

The picture on this page shows many
crayons just after they have come from
the molds. What color are the crayons?

Paper will be put around each crayon.
Then the crayons will be put into boxes
and sent to city shops and schools.

Do you have a box of crayons to use in school? What color do you think you will use up first? Is it the color you like best?

The picture on this page shows many crayons about to be put in boxes. Then they will go to schools and shops all over the world.

When you get a new box of crayons, try not to forget one thing. Never leave them in a place where they will get hot. What happens to crayons if they stay too long in a hot place?

# A New Kind of Picture

Look at the picture on this page.
The girl has just learned how to make
a new kind of picture.

This picture is called a rubbing.
A rubbing is made by rubbing a pencil
or a crayon over something that is
under the paper. What do you think
the girl has placed under her paper?

This rubbing is made by using the side of the crayon. The paper around the crayon must be pulled away before it can be used like this.

To make a rubbing of leaves, place some leaves on a big sheet of paper. Then put another sheet of paper on top of the leaves. After that, rub over the top sheet with the side of a crayon.

Green crayons may be used to show the colors of the leaves in summer. Red and yellow may be used to show the color of fall leaves.

After you make a rubbing of leaves, you may wish to try something harder. See if you can make this rubbing.

Cut a sheet of paper in the shape of a friend's head.

Next, cut bits of paper for the eyes, ears, and lips. Paste them on the head of the cut-out.

Now paste the cut-out onto a sheet of paper. Put a book on top of it and let the paste dry.

When the paste is dry, put a sheet of paper over the cut-out. Now rub with the side of a crayon.

By moving the cut-out around under your paper, you can make many rubbings of the same cut-out.

Friends can work together on one big rubbing. Try making a rubbing of all the children in your room.

You will need a cut-out of each boy and girl in your class at school. Spread out all the cut-outs on a big sheet of paper and paste them down. Then put another sheet of paper over it and make the rubbing.

Make cut-outs of two or three kinds of trees. You can use the same trees over and over. The rubbing can be named "Trees in the Woods."

You can make a rubbing of a city, too.
Make cut-outs of tall apartment buildings.
Make cars, trucks, and buses. Make people
of all ages, walking, running, and. sitting.
Make trees to line the street.

Another rubbing that is fun to make
is one of wild animals. Make cut-outs
of many kinds of wild animals. Spread
them out and paste them down on a big
sheet of paper. Make a rubbing that
shows the animals in a zoo.

## Can You Read This?

"Why is it taking so long to
start the race?" asked Linda.

Just then the race began.
"On your mark! Get set! GO!"

The go-carts came racing down the hill.
Faster and faster they came.

"Jud is winning," cried Linda.

"You must be joking," answered Jan.
"Jud never wins a race."

"Well, he's going to win this time,"
Linda said.

125

Soon another go-cart began coming up
fast in back of Jud's cart. Soon the
other cart was at Jud's side.

"Faster, Jud, faster!" Linda and Jan
yelled together. "Faster, Jud, faster!"

Then it happened! Jud's go-cart went
spinning around.

"Oh, no!" cried Linda. "Jud's cart
is stopping on the grass. What's he
going to do now?"

"Well," said Jan. "It's the same old
story. Hoping Jud will win, but never
getting the wish!"

## Thinking Back

What did you learn about Jud in this story?

This was Jud's first race.

Jud will never race another time.

Jud has bad luck in races.

What do you think happened to Jud's go-cart?

## Talking Things Over

1. How do you think it feels to lose a contest?

2. What does it mean to have bad luck?

# New Ways with Words

Words like **going** are also made from other words. In the word **going, go** is called the **root word**. The **ing** is a **suffix**.
Look for the pattern in each root word in the box below. What is added to each root word before the **ing** is added?

| win | get | stop | spin |
|---|---|---|---|
| winning | getting | stopping | spinning |

The root words in the next box have another pattern. Say the last letter in each root word. Is the letter **e** in the **ing** form?

| race | hope | take | joke |
|---|---|---|---|
| racing | hoping | taking | joking |

**Try This**

Say the root word for each word below.

**hiding    sitting    using    running**

# Animal Talk

# The Jumping Hat

Lightning Bug opened his sleepy eyes.
He pulled out his wings. After sleeping
all the hot summer afternoon, it was good
to be up and about. It was about time to
flash on his bright little light.

But what was that funny little sound?
Bump-bump, bump-bump! Where was that
funny sound coming from?

130

Lightning Bug went to the top of a small tree. He did his best to see what was making the sound.

All Lightning Bug saw was a little hat on the grass. But the hat was a jumping hat.

"Oh, my," said Lightning Bug. "What a funny hat! It jumps! Never before have I seen a hat that jumps."

The hat went bump-bump, bump-bump. Then, from under the hat, came a new sound, "Gr-ump! Gr-ump!"

"Why, that sounds like Frog. But I have never seen him with a hat on!"

The hat was still jumping around.

"Look out!" cried Lightning Bug. "You will bump into a log!"

"Gr-ump! Gr-ump!" said something from under the hat.

"Frog, is that you under the hat?" asked Lightning Bug. "All I can see is two feet."

"Yes," said Frog. "Who are you? I can't see a thing with this hat on."

"I'm Lightning Bug. Why in the world did you put on that hat? It is far too big for you. It comes all the way down to your feet."

"I did not put it on," said Frog. "It fell on me."

"Then, why do you keep the hat on?" asked Lightning Bug.

"I'm stuck!" said Frog. "That is
why I keep it on. How can I get out?"

"Can't you jump out from under it?"
asked Lightning Bug.

"No," said Frog, "it won't work.
When I jump, the hat jumps with me."

"I'll think of a way to free you,"
said Lightning Bug.

At last Lightning Bug had the answer.
"I have it!" he said. "Just hop down
to the pond and jump into the water.
The hat will stay on top of the water
and you will be free.

"I'll flash my light and show you the
way to the pond," said Lightning Bug.

"Just how will that help? I can't
see your light from under this hat,"
said Frog.

Lightning Bug went on thinking. Then
he said, "You can't use your eyes under
the hat, but you can use your ears.
You need some sounds to follow, Frog.
My friend Bee is sleeping now, but
I'll get him up."

As soon as Bee opened his sleepy
eyes, Lightning Bug asked him to help.
Bee was happy to help his friends.
The three of them, one after another,
went down to the pond.
Lightning Bug went first, flashing
his bright light to show the way.
Bee followed Lightning Bug, buzzing,
buzzing, buzzing. Last of all came
Frog, going bump-bump under the hat.

Flash-flash, flash-flash-flash.
Buzz-buzz, buzz-buzz-buzz.
Bump-bump, bump-bump, gr-ump!
Then splash!
Frog jumped into the pond.

The hat stayed on top of the water
when Frog jumped into the pond. Frog
swam out from under the hat and came
up and sat on a log.

"My good friends," he said. "How glad
I am to be free of that hat! I'll never
forget you as long as I live."

# Egbert Learns to Quack

Egbert was a bright duck. He swam as well as all the other little ducks. He walked as well as they did, too.

But one thing about Egbert was odd. He had never learned to quack!

The old ducks said it was because Egbert was hatched in a hen's nest. The little ducks said that Egbert was not very bright.

But Egbert had no real need for
quacking. He lived on a good farm,
where he had good things to eat.
He had a little pond, where he swam.
Why did he need to learn to quack?

One day Egbert's mother saw him at
the pond. He was about to take a big
red berry from a green plant.

"Egbert, I have never seen a duck like
you!" said his mother. "How can you be
a real duck when you can't quack? Come,
now, I will teach you. Do as I do."

Mother Duck opened her bill and went
"Quack, quack, quack!"

Egbert opened his bill and got set.
But the big red berry had stuck in the
back of his bill. The sound he made
was not a quack at all.

"You sound just like a chicken!"
cried Egbert's mother. And away she
went, quacking like mad. "But please
keep trying," she yelled back.

Just then, Egbert saw a big green
grasshopper. A grasshopper was a big
treat, and so Egbert jumped for it.
But the grasshopper jumped first and
got away.

The next grasshopper that Egbert saw
jumped on a rock. Egbert went after it.

As Egbert jumped, his leg got stuck
in some wire. He pulled, and he pulled,
and he pulled. But the wire cut his
poor leg. Then he bit at the wire, but
this just cut his bill.

"I'm stuck," said Egbert to himself.
"I must get help. But what can I do?"

A white kitten came by. "Why don't
you say me-ow?" she said. "That is what
I say when I need help. I can teach
you how to say it."

"Please don't treat me like a kitten,"
said Egbert. "After all, I'm a duck, and
ducks don't sound like kittens. This is
the way a duck sounds."

Egbert opened his bill. "Quack!
Quack! Quack!" he went.

A little girl who lived on the farm
came running to Egbert. In no time
at all, she had Egbert's leg free.

From that day, Egbert swam like
a duck, he walked like a duck, and he
quacked all the time. He was a real
duck after all.

# Parnell the Pet

Parnell Pig had never seen the world, and he began to wonder what it was like. One night as he was sniffing around the farmyard, he saw a way to get out.

In no time at all, he was on his way up the road.

When it began to rain, Parnell crawled into a building by the side of the road. Soft sounds came from the building, but Parnell did not wonder about them a bit. He was too sleepy for that.

The next morning just before sunup,
a red rooster went "Cock-a-doodle-doo!"
Parnell opened his eyes and saw that he
was in a hen house.

Soon a funny old lady in a long dress
came into the hen house. She tripped
over Parnell and just about fell down.
Parnell jumped to get out of her way.

"You silly hen," she cried, looking
down at Parnell. "Get out of my way."

"How can she think that I'm a hen?"
wondered Parnell.

Parnell looked at the lady as she
went from nest to nest, getting eggs.
On her way out of the hen house,
she bumped right into the door.

"Her eyes must be very bad,"
said Parnell to himself. "I think
she needs some eyeglasses."

Parnell stayed on in the hen house
for a time. He did not like the food,
because it was just stuff for hens, and
it was very hard to chew. He asked the
funny old lady to bring him better food.
But her ears were no better than her
eyes, and so Parnell still went hungry.

144

Soon Parnell was hungry all the time.
He had to have something else to eat.
And so, he made plans to leave the old
lady's farm.

When the night came for Parnell Pig
to leave the farm, luck was not with him.
The old lady had set a basket of eggs
by the door, and Parnell bumped into it.
He turned over the basket and frightened
all the chickens. They began to make all
kinds of wild sounds.

"A fox is in the hen house!" the old lady cried. She raced out of the house with a long stick. "I'll get you, you chicken robber!"

Parnell wondered how she could see a fox when her eyes were so bad.

Parnell ran fast, out of the hen house and down the path. All went well until he came to the road. Then down he went. His leg got stuck in some wire. He pulled and cried, but he could not get out.

He wondered when it would get light. He wished the sun would come up so he could see how to free himself.

When daylight came, so did the little
old lady. She was just about on top of
Parnell before she saw him. If he had not
cried out, she would never have seen him.

"Why, you poor little thing!" she said.
"What is the matter? Why are you crying?"
And she got down to free him.

"I'll take you home and make you well,"
she said as she picked him up.

"But I'm not a chicken," said Parnell.

The old lady laughed as she went to
the house. "What a silly thing to say,"
she answered. "I can see that you are
not a chicken."

"And I'm not a fox," said Parnell.

"I can see that, too," laughed the lady.

From then on, Parnell had a happy home.
He lived in the house with the old lady.
She would make jokes and sing songs to him.
And she gave him all kinds of good food.

When they went outside, Parnell Pig
would walk in front of the old lady.
By walking in front of her, he could
keep her from bumping into things.

Parnell soon stopped trying to tell the
old lady that he was a pig. She was so
kind to him that it did not matter now.

"I'm so glad you are staying with me,"
the old lady said many times. "I like
having a dog like you, but I wish you
could say 'bow-wow' as other dogs do."

# Timothy Turtle

Timothy Turtle lived in the woods by
a river. He was a very old turtle, and
he had lived by the river for many years.
All the animals that lived in the woods
liked him.

Timothy's very best friend was the
green frog. The frog lived by the trunk
of a tree on the bank of the river.

Many days Timothy took the frog on his back for a ride up the river.

Timothy liked to splash in the water. He liked to sit on the bank and sleep in the sun.

But best of all he liked to slide down a bank that was not far from the river.

One morning Timothy went for a slide. The bank was wet from a rain that had come in the night. He slid very fast. On his way down the bank, something happened, and Timothy turned over on his back.

Now, Timothy's shell was very big, and
try as he would, he could not turn over.
So he lay on his back and began to kick
his feet. He kicked and kicked and kicked.
He kicked very hard, but he could not
turn his big shell over.

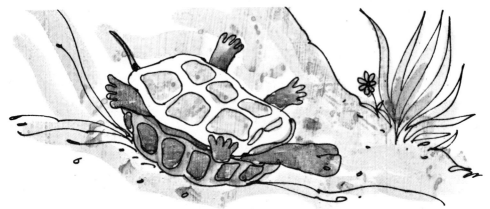

The squirrel who lived in the tall
tree saw Timothy. He came to ask what
had happened.

"What is the matter, Timothy?" asked
the squirrel.

"I fell on my back and can't turn over.
Can you help me?"

But the squirrel was so little he
could not help Timothy.

"I will go for help," said the squirrel.
So he ran into the woods and met the rabbit.

"Please help us," said the squirrel.
"Timothy Turtle fell on his back and
can't turn over."

The squirrel and the rabbit ran
back to Timothy. But they could not
turn him over.

"I will go and get someone else,"
said the squirrel. He ran into the
woods to the home of the woodchuck.

"Come with us," the squirrel said.
"Timothy Turtle fell on his back and
can't turn over."

"I'll be glad to help you," said
the woodchuck. "Wait until I tell
Mrs. Woodchuck where I'm going."

The squirrel and the rabbit waited
for the woodchuck. But when the three
of them got to the river bank, they
could not turn Timothy over.

"I will go and see if I can get
someone else," said the squirrel.
He ran into the woods to the possum,
who was sleeping in the sun.

The squirrel called and called him
until he opened his eyes and looked up.

"Come and help," the squirrel said.
"Timothy Turtle fell on his back and
can't turn over."

"I'll see what I can do," said the possum in a sleepy way. He began to follow the squirrel.

"Will you walk a little faster, Mr. Possum?" asked the squirrel.

"O. K.," said the possum, walking as fast as he could.

So on they went until they came to Timothy. But the squirrel and the rabbit and the woodchuck and the possum could not turn Timothy over.

They sat looking at the turtle and wondering what to do. Timothy was still kicking his feet and trying to turn over.

Now the frog came to see what was going on. He sat on the bank and began to laugh. He laughed so hard that the animals all turned and looked at him.

"What are you laughing about?" asked the squirrel.

"I am laughing at all of you," answered the frog.

"If you think it is so funny, tell us how we can turn Timothy over."

"It is plain to see what you can do," said the frog. "Just take him by the tail and pull him down to the river. When he falls in the water, he will turn over. It is as plain as that."

So the possum held on to Timothy's tail,
and the woodchuck held on to the possum,
and the squirrel held on to the woodchuck,
and the rabbit held on to the squirrel.
They pulled and pulled until they got
Timothy down to the bank of the river.

Splash! went the water, as Timothy
fell in and turned over.

Timothy splashed and swam in the water
until all the mud came off his shell.
Then he came out on the bank and thanked
his friends for helping him.

The rabbit and the woodchuck and the
possum and the squirrel sat on the bank.
They looked at Timothy as he took the
frog on his back for a ride up the river.

# The Elephant on the Bus

The blue bus stopped at the bus stop.
A man got off and an elephant got on.
The bus driver looked at the elephant and
said, "Oh, no, you can't ride on my bus!"

The elephant said, "But I must get
back to the zoo for lunch. I have money
for the ride." And he held out his trunk
with the money in it.

The driver said, "But . . . but . . .
you still can't ride on my bus.
You are too big!"

The elephant looked very sad.
He said, "But I'm just a small elephant.
I won't take up a lot of room. I'll make
myself very small."

The people on the bus asked the driver
to let the elephant come into the bus.
And so at last the driver said, "Well,
all right. You can ride on my bus, but
you may not take up more than one seat."

So the elephant gave his money
to the bus driver and sat down.
He scrunched himself together,
rolled up his long trunk, and
sat as still as he could.

At the next stop, a lady got on and
sat in the seat in front of the elephant.
She had on a red hat with a long, long
feather that went back over the seat
and tickled the elephant's trunk.

As the bus went on, the feather
jiggled up and down, and this tickled
the poor elephant's trunk. The elephant
felt as if he were going to sneeze.

The elephant would have turned away,
but then he would bump the man sitting
next to him. He would have asked the
lady in front of him to take off her hat,
but he would have to unroll his trunk to
say something, and he had no room for that.

The feather went on jiggling
up and down, up and down, and
tickled him more and more.
He felt . . . he felt . . . hanh . . . hanh.
He felt . . . he felt . . . hanh . . . hanh . . .
HANH . . . CHOOOO!

It was a TREMENDOUS sneeze.
The scrunched-up elephant spread out
like a balloon, and his rolled-up trunk
snapped out, and he sneezed the hats
right off the people in the bus.

The red hat with the long, long
feather landed on the driver's head,
and the driver's cap
landed on the elephant's head.
And a big man's hat landed
on a little girl's head.
Each hat in the bus came off
and landed on someone else's head.
The people and the elephant looked
very silly.

The driver stopped the bus, and all the people traded hats until the hats were on the right heads. Then the driver said the elephant would have to get off the bus. All the people said it would be the best thing to do, too.

So the elephant got off the bus and walked back to the zoo. On the way he had another big sneeze, right out in the open, so no one's hat came off.

And from that day on, you never see an elephant on a bus.

# Can You Read This?

"Well," said the queen, looking down at the two boys. "What brings you to the land of the monster?  Speak up!"

"We have come to tame the monster," came the soft small answer.

"Silly boys," laughed the queen. "So you wish to try your hand at something no one else could do. Did no one tell you that monsters are mean?  That this one eats people?"

"He won't eat us," said the taller boy.

"Well, be off with you then," said the queen. "But if you fail, you may never see the light of another day."

The boys were deep in the woods when they picked up the monster's trail.

"Wait," said the smaller boy. "Tell
me your plan before we meet the monster.
How are we going to tame him?"

"To tame a monster, you just tickle
his tail," said the taller boy. "Then
he will turn into a good monster."

The smaller boy felt sick. "Tickle
his tail!" he cried. "What do you mean?
This monster has no tail. He has another
head where the tail would be."

"You don't say!" said the taller boy.
"Then no wonder no one could tame him.
You can't tickle a monster's tail when
he has no tail. Come on, we had better
head for home."

And off they ran.

## Thinking Back

How did the boy plan to tame the monster?

What kind of monster did you picture
as you were reading the story?

## Talking Things Over

1. Tell about a monster you have read
   about or seen in a picture.
2. How can you tell that a story is
   make-believe?

# New Ways with Words

You have learned the word **eye,** and
you can tell what it means. But what
if your mother asked you to **keep an eye
on the baby**? Would you look for an **eye**
to put on the baby? What would you do?

## Try This

Read each sentence below.
Then tell what the underlined words
mean in each sentence.

1. "So you wish to <u>try your hand at</u>
   something no one else could do."

2. "Well, <u>be off with you</u> then!"

3. "But if you fail, you may never
   <u>see the light of another day.</u>"

4. The boys were <u>deep in the woods.</u>

5. They <u>picked up the monster's trail.</u>

## A Word Pattern

All the words in the box have the same pattern. The pattern is a clue to the vowel sounds. Read the words.

| | | | |
|---|---|---|---|
| fail | mean | deep | queen |
| trail | speak | meet | |

Each pattern that is underlined has two vowel letters together. Do all the words in the box have long vowel sounds?

Many words with two vowel letters together have long vowel sounds.

## Try This

Two words in the box have rhyming sounds that are spelled with the same letters. What are these rhyming words?

Two other words in the box have rhyming sounds spelled with different letters. What are these two words?

# Good Things to Eat

# Raisins

Are you hungry when you come home from school in the afternoon? Do you go to the kitchen and look around for something to eat? What kind of food do you look for?

Some children look for cake to eat after school. Some look for candy. Cake and candy are sweet foods, and so children like them.

Some sweet foods are better for you
than candy and cake. Raisins are sweet,
and they are very good for you.

If you can, look at some raisins now.
You may see one with a bit of stem on it.
The stem shows that the raisin came from
a plant.

What kind of a plant do you think a
raisin comes from? Is the plant a vine?

The plants that raisins come from
are grape vines.

Grape vines are planted in long rows.
In summer many big green leaves grow
on the vines. It takes three or four years
before a new vine will have grapes.

At first the grapes are small and not
very sweet. But as they grow they get
bigger and sweeter until they are ripe.

When the grapes are ripe, they are
picked by hand. Then they are spread
out to dry in the hot sun. To dry,
the grapes need many days of hot sun
and no rain.

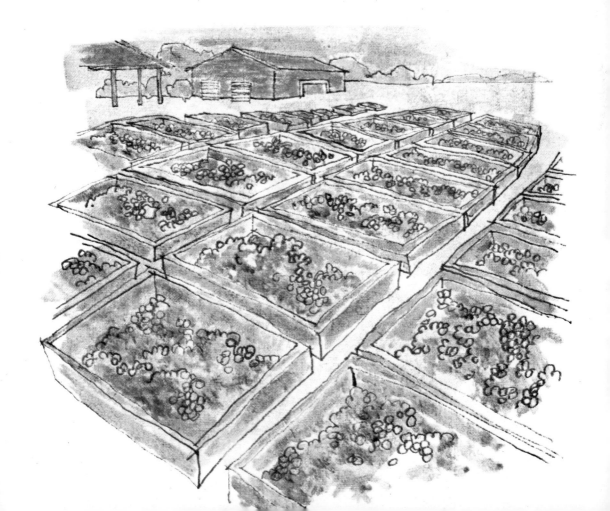

Grapes get darker and sweeter as they dry. In time, they are raisins.

The dry, sweet raisins are sent to a packing house. At the packing house the stems are pulled from the raisins. Then the raisins are cleaned.

The cleaned raisins are packed in small boxes. And then they are sent off to places where people will buy them.

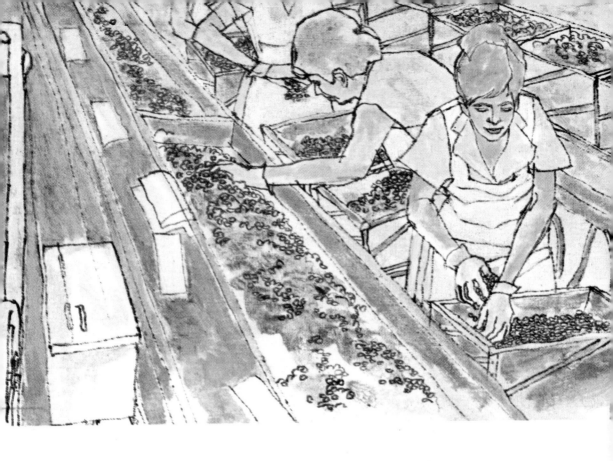

We can buy a box of raisins for very little money. But many years ago, this was not so.

Long ago, it took a lot of money to buy raisins. Poor people could never buy raisins because they did not have the money. And so, long ago, raisins were just for rich people.

What luck for us that we can now buy raisins for very little money!

# An Apple a Day

"An apple a day keeps the doctor away."
This is an old saying that people have
used for years. The man who first said
this was trying to tell us something.
Was this his way of saying that apples
are good for us? What do you think?

If you do eat an apple a day, could
you still need a doctor sometimes?

Apple trees grow well in many parts of the world. But no other country has as many apple trees as this country has.

Yet many years ago this country had no apple trees at all. This was the time when Indians lived where we live now. The Indians long ago had never seen an apple tree.

Then one day white people came to live in this new land. Some of the first white people who came had apple seeds with them. Some had small apple trees to plant, too. Soon after the people landed, they planted the seeds and trees.

The picture shows
an apple tree
as it looks
in spring.
In spring
apple trees
are filled with
little flowers.
Bees buzz from one
flower to another
all around the tree.

In time, the flowers fall.
Then small green apples begin
to grow. For each flower that
falls from the tree, an apple
will grow in its place.

At first the apples are small, green,
and very hard. But as they keep growing,
they get bigger and softer until they
are ripe. By the time they are ripe,
the apples are sweet and good to eat.

Each spring and summer, apple trees must be sprayed. The spray keeps bugs from laying eggs in the flowers and on the trunk.

The apples are picked in the fall. The ripe apples are cleaned and packed in baskets and boxes. Then people load them on big trucks. The loads of apples are sent to places where you and other people can buy them.

As winter comes, leaves begin to fall from trees. All winter long, apple trees, like many other trees, wait for spring. When the next spring comes around, the trees will bear new flowers, new leaves, and more apples to eat.

# Fun with Apples

Apples are good to eat. But that is not all they can be used for.

Apples are sometimes used for games. One game is "Duck for the Apple."

To play this game, put two or three apples in a tub of water. The apples will stay on top of the water, because apples float.

With your hands in back of you, duck your head into the tub and try to get one of the floating apples. Don't be too surprised if you get a little wet when you play this game.

The one who gets an apple first is the one who wins the game.

Another game to play with apples
is called "Apple Race." You will need
some friends and one apple for each.

Ask the children who are going to
play to get down on the grass in a row.
Place an apple in front of each boy
and girl. Tell the children that each
is to roll his own apple without using
hands or feet. Then tell them how far
they must go to win the race.

"On your mark! Get set! Go!"
Look at the children rolling the apples!
What a race! I wonder who will win?

# Johnny Appleseed

He must have looked funny as he walked in the woods. He had an old pot for a hat and a sack on his back. He made friends with animals, and he liked to sleep out under the stars.

He was a plain man, but he was good, and people liked him. Day after day, he walked many long miles. He planted apple trees and gave away apple seeds.

For years no one had called him by his real name. They just called him Johnny Appleseed.

As a boy, Johnny had lived on a farm. But he never liked to stay in one place. He liked moving around. And so, one fine morning he set out.

He had with him a pot to cook in. When he was not cooking, he used the pot for a hat. He had other things he owned in an old sack. And he had small bags filled with apple seeds.

He was eating an apple as he walked down the country road. He picked out the seeds and put them into one of his little bags.

Johnny made up a song to sing as he
walked down the country road.

Eat the ripe red apple,
This is what you need.
Eat the apple, eat the apple,
Do not eat the seed.

First you eat the apple,
Then you plant the seed.
Grow a tall new apple tree,
That is what you need.

Johnny came to the end of the road.
Where the road ended, the woods began.
Johnny did not stop. He walked right
on into the woods, as the Indians did.

When the sun began to sink in the sky,
Johnny stopped for the night. He took off
his funny hat and used it to cook his food.
Then he took some things out of his sack
and made his bed on the ground. Soon he
was on his back, looking up at the sky.

One by one, the little stars came out.
Then the big round moon came up, and the
trees made shadows in the moonlight.

Johnny was happy. This was a place
he liked. With a smile, he went to sleep.

The next morning Johnny was up with
the sun. He packed up his things and
was soon moving on.

Far from his home he met a father, mother, and some children. They were building a log house. Johnny stopped and gave them some of his apple seeds. They were glad to get the seeds, and they asked him to stay for the night.

He stayed, but he would not sleep in the house. "My place is under the trees," he said.

The next day Johnny was on his way. He walked on, planting apple seeds as he went. He made friends with the people he met. He gave them seeds and showed them how to do the planting.

Johnny did this year after year. He went from place to place planting apple seeds and teaching people how to grow apple trees.

One cold winter day, Johnny fell down
in the woods. He lay on the ground in
the snow for a long time.

At last an Indian woman saw Johnny
on the ground. She shouted for help.
Her shouts made other Indians come fast.
They picked up Johnny and took him back
to the place where they lived.

The Indians looked after Johnny all
that winter. When spring came, he was well.
He thanked his Indian friends for looking
after him. Then away he went, with his
little bags of apple seeds.

Johnny walked on for many, many years.
His work helped to bring apples to many
parts of our country, and he was proud
of his work. He was proud to see so many
apple trees growing in our country.

The next time you eat an apple, you
can thank Johnny Appleseed.

# Peanuts

Did you ever have monkey nuts for your lunch? Did you ever eat goobers? Did you ever take the shell off a ground nut?

No? You don't think so?

Well, then, did you ever eat peanuts or take the shells off them? You did?

Then you have had monkey nuts, goobers, and ground nuts. They are just other names for peanuts.

We call them peanuts, but they are
not real nuts. They are like green peas.
Peanuts, like peas, grow on small plants.

Look at some peanuts in the shells.
Then look at some peas in the pods.
As you see, the shells are like pods,
and peanuts are like peas. The nuts
are the seeds of the peanut plant.

To grow peanuts, people must first
plow the ground. Peanuts are planted
in the plowed ground. Before long,
little peanut plants begin to grow.

Soon the plants have many small yellow flowers. They look a bit like the garden flowers called sweet peas.

A peanut flower opens at sunup. But it falls by noon, and so it is not open very long.

After the flower falls, the flower stem grows fast. It turns and grows down into the ground. The seed pod then grows underground on the stem. Each pod has from one to six seeds.

One peanut plant has many flower stems growing underground. And so, many pods, with many nuts in them, may come from just one plant.

When the seed pods are ripe, the
plant is pulled out of the ground.
It is then put in the sun to dry.
It turns brown as it gets dry.
When the plant is dry and brown,
the pods are picked off.

When the peanuts are first picked,
they do not look at all like nuts.
They are milk white and very soft.
It is not until we roast them that
they look and smell like peanuts.

Peanuts may be roasted at home in
a hot oven. How good they are to eat
when they are still hot!

# Plant Doctor

When the boy was small, he lived on
a farm.  He helped with the planting
and the picking.  He looked after the
garden, and he helped in the house too.

The one thing he liked best was to
study plants.  He would walk in the
woods and study the trees and flowers.
He liked to study farm plants too, and
he learned how to make them grow better.

When his many friends had plants that
were not growing well, they sent for him.
He could make a sick plant well. People
called him the little plant doctor.

The boy had no teacher, and so he had
to learn things for himself. He had a
spelling book, and he learned to spell.
He had a story book, and he learned
to read.

One day a kind man gave him a book
about plants. But the boy could not
read all the hard words in the book.
How he would enjoy going to school!
But the school was too far away.

It was not until he was ten years of
age that he found a way to go to school.
To do so, he had to leave his home and
his friends. He had very little money.

That first winter was a hard one.
He worked for his food by doing odd
jobs for people who would take him in.
Many winter nights he went to sleep
cold and hungry.


At school, children laughed at him.
They laughed because he looked so poor
and because he could not do all the things
they could do. But when they saw how
fast the small, dark boy could learn,
the laughing soon stopped.

The boy went from grade to grade
and from one school to the next one.
He still enjoyed plants, and he learned
more and more about them. One of the
plants he learned about was the peanut.

When his school days were over,
he was a real plant doctor.  His name
was George Washington Carver.

Dr. Carver soon gave more and more
time to his study of peanuts.  At that
time, people did not grow many peanuts.
The ones they did grow were used as
food for farm animals.

People had not yet learned of the
many ways that peanuts can be used.
And they had not yet found out what
a real treat roasted peanuts can be.

195

On many old farms, people planted the
same thing year after year. This made
the soil very poor. At times, the soil
was so poor that plants did not grow well.
But Dr. Carver found out how poor soil
could be made better.

"Plant more peanuts," he said.

"Peanuts!" answered the farm people.
"What man wants to grow more 'goobers?
What good are they? We want to grow
something that will bring us money."

"The peanut is one of the best foods
in all the world," said Dr. Carver.
And he began to teach farm people the
things he had learned about peanuts.

We will never forget Dr. Carver,
the famous plant doctor. From his work,
people all over our country learned how
to grow and use peanuts.

They learned that as peanuts grow,
they make poor soil better.

They learned that dry peanut plants
are good food for farm animals.

They learned that peanuts are rich
in oil.

They learned to use peanut oil
to make many kinds of things.

And they learned how to make the
best peanut butter in the world!

# Can You Read This?

Can you think what it would be like
if we had no alphabet? With no alphabet
we would have no good way of writing.
And then we would have no books to read.

Many, many years ago this was the
way it was. People did not write at all.
They could not write because they had
not discovered that letters could be used
to stand for words.

The first writing that people did was a
kind of picture-writing. They tried to make
a picture for each word. But it was hard to
draw pictures for some words. Can you
draw pictures for words like **best,** or **still,**
or **answer?**

In time, people tried to think of a better
way to write.

Picture-Writing of American Indians

"Words have sounds," they said.
"We need to think of something to
stand for each sound in our words."
And that is when the first alphabet
began, many, many years ago.

The alphabet we use is not the same
as the first alphabet. It is not the
same because, over the years, ways were
found to make the alphabet better.
For one thing, people began to use
letters that were not so hard to write.
And so, after many years we got our
ABC's — an alphabet that works just fine.

## Thinking Back

Did you understand the main ideas as you were reading the last two pages? If you did, then you can pick the title that is best. What is it?

> People Who Could Not Write
> The Story of Our Alphabet
> The First Picture-writing

What is an alphabet?

Why was picture-writing not a good way of writing?

## Talking Things Over

1. Tell about a sign language or code you share with your friends.
2. Make up a word that isn't a real word. Tell what letters will stand for the sounds in your word.

# Two Is a Team

BY LORRAINE AND JERROLD BEIM

Ted and Paul were friends. They played
together each day after school.

"We are just the same age!" they said
to Ted's mother when they played
at his house.

"And we are just the same size,"
they showed Paul's mother when they
played at his house.

One afternoon they were playing
on the street and saw some boys go
racing by on coasters.

"I wish I had a coaster," Ted said.

And then Paul had an idea. "Let's
make one," he cried.

"I have an old roller skate we
could use for the wheels," Ted said.

"I have a box and some wood at my house," Paul said.

They ran home as fast as they could for the things to make the coaster.

When they came back, Ted began to nail the roller skate wheels to a piece of wood.

"That's not the way. Let me do it," Paul said.

"I can do it myself!" Ted answered, and he would not let Paul help him.

Paul took the hammer and began to nail the box to the piece of wood.

"You are not doing it right," Ted said.

"I am too!" Paul answered, and he would not let Ted help him.

"Let me have the hammer," Ted said.

"I'm going to put on the next piece
of wood."

"No, you won't," Paul answered.
"I'm going to do it." Paul tried to keep
the hammer, but Ted pulled it away
from him.

"I'm not going to make a coaster
with you." Paul hit Ted.

"Who wants to make one with you?"
Ted kicked Paul. Paul took his box and
piece of wood. Ted took his roller skate.

They were so mad at each other they
did not think to say good-bye.

When Ted got home, he began to make his own coaster. He got an old box and a piece of wood and made the coaster the way he wanted to.

When Paul got home, he began making
his own coaster. He got some old baby
carriage wheels and made the coaster
the way he wanted to.

The boys met on the street the next day with the new coasters.

"My coaster is better than yours," Paul said.

"It is not. My coaster is better than yours," Ted said. "Let us have a race and see!"

They took the two coasters to the top of a hill.

"On your mark—get set—go!" they called.

The race was on! Down—down the hill
they went on the coasters—so fast they
could not stop.

Down—down the hill they went—
so fast they did not see the lady crossing
the street with a big bag of groceries.
They bumped into her, and her bag of
groceries went spilling to the ground.

Down—down the hill they went—
so fast they did not see the little girl
crossing the street with her doll carriage.
They bumped right into the carriage, and
the doll went spilling to the ground.

Down—down the hill they went—
so fast they did not see the man crossing
the street with his dog. They just about
bumped into him and the dog ran away.

Down—down the hill they went—
and when they came to the end of the
block—what do you think happened?

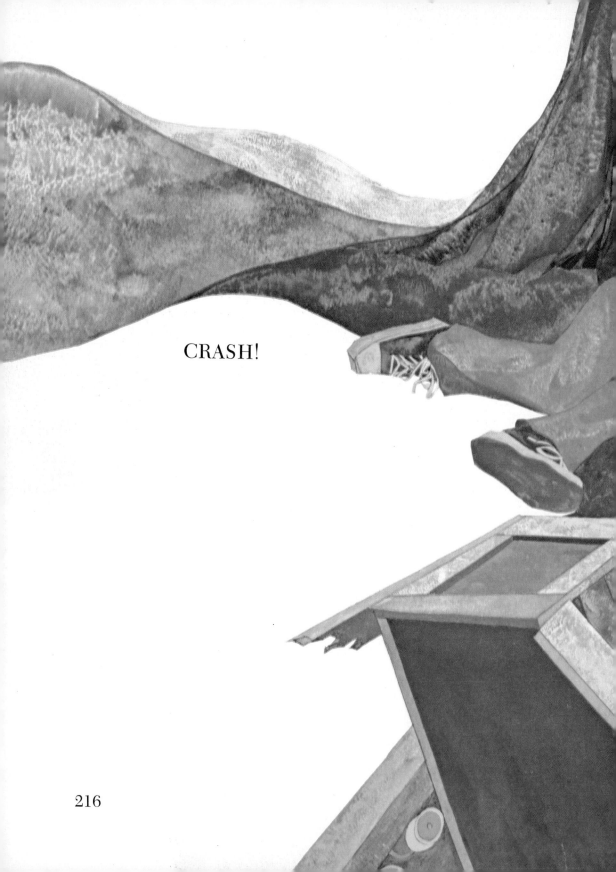

CRASH!

"My wheels came off!" Ted cried.

"My box came off!" Paul said.

Then they looked up and they saw

A lady,

a man,

and a little girl.

"You made me drop my groceries,
and I spilled the milk," the lady said.

"You bumped my carriage, and my doll's
leg came off," the little girl said.

"My dog ran away, and when I got him
he had lost his leash," the man said.
"You boys will have to pay for what
you did."

Poor Ted and Paul!  They had no idea
how they were going to pay for what
they did.  They set out for home together,
looking very sad, and taking the pieces
of the coasters with them.

Just before they got home, they saw
a sign on the door of a food shop.

"Why don't we get a job?" Ted said.

They went into the food shop.
"Could you use two delivery boys?"
they asked.

"Well, I could," the man at the food
shop said. "But you have to have your
own wagon to deliver the groceries."

"We have no wagon," Paul said.

Then Ted had a fine idea. "We will be
back to work with a wagon tomorrow,"
he said.

"A wagon! Where will we get a wagon?"
Paul asked when they went out.

"We will make one," Ted answered.
"Out of the coasters!"

And they did!  They worked hard
the rest of the day building a wagon.
Paul let Ted help him put the box on.
Ted let Paul help him put the wheels on.
And together they made a fine wagon!

Each day after school they worked together. Sometimes Ted steered the wagon and Paul delivered the groceries. Sometimes Paul steered and Ted delivered the groceries.

They paid the lady back for her food. They paid the little girl back for her doll. They paid the man back for his dog's leash.

And they learned how to drive the wagon
down a hill—zig-zagging around the people
with groceries, carriages, or dogs.

That was the best fun of all!

D E F G H I J 7 8 9 0 1 2